English Workbook

for

Fifth Grade

GW00778101

Ted Warren

The Teenage Edge

Published by The Teenage-Edge & Company

www.teenage-edge.org

ISBN: 978-0-991-58472-7

Printed in the United States of America

Contents

Introduction

This workbook teaches you how to improve your English whenever you write, read, or speak. With it, you will practice writing the language using grammar as your guide. The goal is not only to know what an adverb is, but to use adverbs powerfully when you write and speak! This is true of all aspects of grammar.

In this workbook you will begin by discovering the parts of speech in sentences. Then you learn the difference between direct and indirect speech in order to make better use of them. The next chapter brings you into the active voice and the passive voice where you will discover how the subject of the sentence uses the verb actively and then how the subject is passively influenced by the verb.

The largest chapter introduces you to verbs in complex tenses. This enables you to speak and write in the correct moment of time. It improves your reading because you will more easily understand authors who describe events in many different times. The following chapters cover adverbs, conjunctions, interjections, pronouns, prepositions, nouns, and finally adjectives. The final chapters teach you punctuation rules and how to write standardized letters.

The quality of your English will improve as you learn to use the language well. You will use the rules of grammar to help you know that you know how the language works. The English language has evolved over many centuries in many different countries, and there are often exceptions to the rules that you will also discover.

Remember that my examples are not important; they merely help you practice. Their goal is to continually develop your knowledge of grammar, so that you can write your own, new examples.

Ted Warren
Scranton, Pennsylvania

Parts of Speech

Nouns (n) denote persons, places, or things.

Adjectives (adj.) show the qualities of the nouns.

Pronouns (p) replace nouns and have many subclasses: personal, possessive, demonstrative, relative, interrogative, and indefinite.

Verbs (v) denote actions and states of being.

Adverbs (adv.) modify other adverbs, adjectives, or verbs.

Prepositions (prep.) determine the relationships between words

Conjunctions (conj.) are words that connect other words, phrases, or clauses.

Interjections (interj.) are words that show great feeling and may stand outside ordinary sentences.

Articles (art.) are three words: a, an, the. *A* and *an* are indefinite articles. *The* is the definite article.

Memory Exercise 1

Learn the parts of speech and their abbreviations by heart.

Exercise 1

Use the abbreviations to define the part of speech of each word in the sentence.

Set the abbreviation above the word;

n v adv.
Ian runs quickly.

1. Why did he build the raft?
2. We must build another raft.
3. The tree is very tall.
4. Where did the boy live?
5. They found an arrow.
6. The name of the girl is Julia.
7. They were jumping in the pool on the hill.
8. The dragons are green and red.
9. Ah, Merlin told us about the land of the near future.

Exercise 2

Write the correct part of speech above each word in the following sentences.

1. I love my older brother.

2. Go!

3. He drove fifty miles.

4. I have one dozen fish.

5. Five hundred balloons flew high into the sky.

6. I want to be a good policeman.

7. He wants to be a mechanical engineer.

8. She is a successful gardener.

9. He is our family doctor.

10. I will give him my favorite book.

11. They used to be the owners of the car.

12. Wow! Here comes the evening sunset.

13. The Syracuse football player scored a touchdown.

14. She will ask the politician a difficult question.

15. I know a good answer for you.

16. I will give you the book.

17. Hey! Go jump in the lake!

18. My father is a trial lawyer in Allentown.

19. She saw her new hat in the mirror.

20. I asked my uncle an important question.

21. The children excused themselves from the table.

22. The boy criticized me for making the mistake.

23. The visitors helped find some water.

24. My mother always invites Aunt Polly to lunch.

25. He is teaching Spanish.

26. Bake a pie at home.

Direct and Indirect Speech

Examples:

Direct Speech	She asked me, "When are we going to leave?"
Indirect Speech	She asked me when we were going to leave.
Direct Speech	You said, "I will help you!"
Indirect Speech	You said you would help me.
Direct Speech	Mark asked me, "Why do you want to study Chinese?"
Indirect Speech	Mark asked me why I wanted to study Chinese.
Direct Speech	The Comets boasted, "How could we not win?"
Indirect Speech	The Comets boasted that there was no reason that they could not win.
Direct Speech Question	"Did Maria's horse win a prize?" the owner asked.
Indirect Speech Question	The owner asked whether Maria's horse had won a prize.

Note: The rules for writing direct speech are in the Punctuation Rules section on page 87-88.

Exercise 3

Write three more examples of indirect questions.

1. ______________________________

2. ______________________________

3. ______________________________

Exercise 4

Use the following nouns to make three sentences in direct speech.

Narragansett Bay

____

____

____

Cape Cod Bay

____

____

____

Use the following nouns to make three sentences in indirect speech.

Chesapeake Bay

Kailua Bay

Use the following noun to make three sentences using a direct question.

Lake Ontario

Active and Passive Voice

Active sentences:
I write poems.

She writes to her sister.

She has written her sister.

Martin is cleaning his room.

Passive sentences:
The football is kicked.

The football was kicked.

The room is being cleaned by Martin.

Exercise 5

Identify whether the sentence is passive or active and write it next to the sentence.

1. She stomped out of the room.______________________________

2. To smother it, the fire was stomped on by us.___________________

3. We raked the leaves into a pile._____________________________

4. The ball was thrown onto the roof.___________________________

5. She twirled on the bars ten times.______________________________

6. The oven was turned on to warm our dinner.____________________

Grammar Rule 1

Shall is rarely used in American English. All verbs can be used in both the active and passive voice in the present tense, the past tense, and the future tense.

	Present	**Past**	**Future**
Active	I kick.	I kicked.	I shall kick. I will kick.
Passive	The ball is kicked.	The ball was kicked.	The ball shall be kicked.

Figure 1.

Comparing active and passive sentences:

You hit the ball.	active
The ball was hit by you.	passive
The water surges through the rapids.	active
The rapids were surged through by the water.	passive
The block was run around by the boy.	passive
The boy ran around the block.	active
You kick the ball.	active
The ball was kicked by you.	passive
The kayak hit the rock.	active
The rock was hit by the kayak.	passive
The block was driven around by the car driver.	passive
The car driver drove around the block.	active

Exercise 6

Choose a verb and use it in an active and a passive sentence.

1. borrow

    I am borrowing your car. ___________________

    The car is being borrowed for the day. _______________________

2.

    ____

    ____

3.

    ____

    ____

4.

    ____

    ____

Exercise 7

Turn these sentences into the passive voice.

1. She brings her book. ______________________________

2. She is bringing the doll.______________________________

3. She brought the rope.______________________________

4. She has brought the pen. ______________________________

5. She was bringing the car. ______________________________

6. She had brought the truck. ______________________________

7. She will bring the ring. ______________________________

8. I will bring the key. ______________________________

9. She will have brought the map. ______________________________

10. She had broken her thumb. ______________________________

11. She will kick the can. ______________________________

12. I will water the flowers. ______________________________

13. She is listening to the music. ______________________________

Exercise 8

Complete the passive or active sentence.

The tennis ball was hit by the boy.	passive
The boy ________________________ tennis ball.	active
The rope ________________________ by the girl.	passive
The girl jumped the rope.	active
The book was read by the woman.	passive
The woman ______________________ the book.	active
The food was grown by the family.	passive
The family _______________________ the food.	active
The house was bought by the family.	passive
The family ____________________________ the house.	active
The bike was _____________________ by the girl.	passive
The girl rode the bike.	active
The newspaper was bought by the woman.	passive
The woman ______________________ the newspaper.	active
The dinner was prepared by the father.	passive
The father ____________________________ the dinner.	active
The hat was bought by the grandfather.	passive
The grandfather ________________________ the hat.	active

Verbs in Complex Tenses

A. Almost Complete Irregular Verb List

Irregular verbs are learned in the present tense, the past tense, and the perfect tense. The perfect tense indicates that something has happened. Use this list when you answer questions in this workbook.

Present Tense	***Past Tense***	***Perfect Tense***
arise	*arose*	*arisen*
(be) am, is	*was, were*	*been*
beat	*beat*	*beaten*
become	*became*	*become*
begin	*began*	*begun*
behold	*beheld*	*beheld*
bend	*bent*	*bent*
bereave	*bereaved, bereft*	*bereaved, bereft*
bid	*bade, bid*	*bidden, bid*
bind	*bound*	*bound*
bite	*bit*	*bitten*
bleed	*bled*	*bled*
blow	*blew*	*blown*
break	*broke*	*broken*
breed	*bred*	*bred*
bring	*brought*	*brought*
build	*built*	*built*
burn	*burnt, burned*	*burned, burnt*
burst	*burst*	*burst*
buy	*bought*	*bought*

Present Tense	*Past Tense*	*Perfect Tense*
cast	*cast*	*cast*
catch	*caught*	*caught*
choose	*chose*	*chosen*
cling	*clung*	*clung*
come	*came*	*come*
cost	*cost*	*cost*
creep	*crept*	*crept*
cut	*cut*	*cut*
dig	*dug*	*dug*
dive	*dived or dove*	*dived*
do	*did*	*done*
draw	*drew*	*drawn*
dream	*dreamed, dreamt*	*dreamed, dreamt*
drink	*drank*	*drunk*
drive	*drove*	*driven*
dwell	*dwelt, dwelled*	*dwelt, dwelled*
eat	*ate*	*eaten*
fall	*fell*	*fallen*
feed	*fed*	*fed*
feel	*felt*	*felt*
fight	*fought*	*fought*
find	*found*	*found*
flee	*fled*	*fled*
fling	*flung*	*flung*
fly	*flew*	*flown*
forbid	*forbade*	*forbidden*
forget	*forgot*	*forgotten*
forgive	*forgave*	*forgiven*
forsake	*forsook*	*forsaken*

Present Tense	***Past Tense***	***Perfect Tense***
freeze	*froze*	*frozen*
get	*got*	*gotten, got*
give	*gave*	*given*
go	*went*	*gone*
grind	*ground*	*ground*
grow	*grew*	*grown*
hang	*hung, hanged*	*hung, hanged*
have, has	*had*	*had*
hear	*heard*	*heard*
hide	*hid*	*hidden*
hit	*hit*	*hit*
hold	*held*	*held*
hurt	*hurt*	*hurt*
keep	*kept*	*kept*
kneel	*knelt*	*knelt*
know	*knew*	*known*
knit	*knitted, knit*	*knitted, knit*
lay (to place)	*laid*	*laid*
lead	*led*	*led*
leap	*leapt*	*leapt*
learn	*learned*	*learned*
leave (to depart)	*left*	*left*
lend	*lent*	*lent*
let	*let*	*let*
lie (to recline)	*lay*	*lain*
light	*lit, lighted*	*lit, lighted*
lose	*lost*	*lost*
make	*made*	*made*
mean	*meant*	*meant*

Present Tense	***Past Tense***	***Perfect Tense***
meet	*met*	*met*
mistake	*mistook*	*mistaken*
overcome	*overcame*	*overcome*
partake	*partook*	*partaken*
pay	*paid*	*paid*
put	*put*	*put*
raise (elevate)	*raised*	*raised*
read	*read*	*read*
rend	*rent*	*rent*
rid	*rid*	*rid*
ride	*rode*	*ridden*
ring	*rang*	*rung*
run	*ran*	*run*
say	*said*	*said*
saw	*sawed*	*sawn*
see	*saw*	*seen*
send	*sent*	*sent*
set	*set*	*set*
sew	*sewed*	*sewn*
shake	*shook*	*shaken*
shave	*shaved*	*shaved, shaven*
shear	*sheared*	*sheared, shorn*
shed	*shed*	*shed*
shine	*shone, shined*	*shone, shined*
shoe	*shod*	*shod*
shoot	*shot*	*shot*
show	*showed*	*shown*
shrink	*shrank*	*shrunk, shrunken*
shut	*shut*	*shut*

Present Tense	***Past Tense***	***Perfect Tense***
sing	*sang*	*sung*
sink	*sank*	*sunk*
sit	*sat*	*sat*
slide	*slid*	*slid*
sling	*slung*	*slung*
slink	*slunk*	*slunk*
slit	*slit*	*slit*
sell	*sold*	*sold*
seek	*sought*	*sought*
sleep	*slept*	*slept*
smell	*smelt, smelled*	*smelt, smelled*
smite	*smote*	*smitten*
sow	*sowed*	*sown*
speed	*sped, speeded*	*sped, speeded*
spend	*spent*	*spent*
spill	*spilled, spilt*	*spilled, spilt*
spin	*spun*	*spun*
spit	*spat*	*spat*
split	*split*	*split*
spoil	*spoiled, spoilt*	*spoiled, spoilt*
spread	*spread*	*spread*
spring	*sprang*	*sprung*
stand	*stood*	*stood*
stick	*stuck*	*stuck*
stink	*stank*	*stunk*
strew	*strewed*	*strewn*
stride	*strode*	*stridden*
strike	*struck*	*struck, stricken*
strive	*strove*	*striven*

Present Tense	**Past Tense**	**Perfect Tense**
sweep	*swept*	*swept*
swell	*swelled*	*swollen, swelled*
swim	*swam*	*swum*
take	*took*	*taken*
teach	*taught*	*taught*
tell	*told*	*told*
think	*thought*	*thought*
thrust	*thrust*	*thrust*
thrive	*throve, thrived*	*thriven, thrived*
tread	*trod*	*trodden, trod*
understand	*understood*	*understood*
weep	*wept*	*wept*
wind	*wound*	*wound*
withhold	*withheld*	*withheld*
withstand	*withstood*	*withstood*
write	*wrote*	*written*

Figure 2.

Exercise 9

Write three paragraphs using irregular verbs.

Exercise 10

Find irregular verbs with the same endings or sound in the present tense. Then write them in the past and perfect tenses.

Present Tense	***Past Tense***	***Perfect Tense***
forsake		
partake		

Present Tense	***Past Tense***	***Perfect Tense***
strive		

Present Tense	***Past Tense***	***Perfect Tense***
sweep		

Present Tense	***Past Tense***	***Perfect Tense***
tell		

Figure 3.

B. Helping Verbs

These are the standard helping verbs: to be, have, can, could, do, shall, will, may, might, must, shall, should, will, would, need, ought to, and used to.

Here are some examples:

You can stay up. You could stay up.
You may not now. You might not now. You must not now.
She ought to listen.
He should sing.
They will respond. They would respond, if they could.

Exercise 11

Write sentences using each helping verb mentioned above.

Grammar Rule 2

The helping verb *will* is used to show willingness, determination, promise, and command:

He will help you.
She will do what is best.
He will deliver the speech.
We will do as I say!

Grammar Rule 3

In British English shall is commonly used. In American English, it is rarely used being only found in formal documents and for particular emphasis in common speech.

Shall we go!
We shall overcome!

C. Complicated Verb Tenses

The more complicated verb forms present new aspects of the three basic tenses: present, past, and future. They cross in and out of the various relationships in time; for example, when I say, "I cut wood". Here, I return to the action as it happened. This is the past tense. If I say, " I had cut wood", I return to the time in the past when the action was already finished. This is the past perfect tense, a finished picture projected into the past. We reflect upon the picture with our thoughts.

In the perfect tense, something has happened in the present. The action is within a finished picture in the present. Therefore we use the helping verb, *to have*, in the present tense. The perfect tense, *I have cut wood*, is in the present, but it is a completed action.

The past perfect tense, *I had cut wood*, is in the past and is a completed action. Something has happened in the past.

In the future perfect tense, the sentence, *I will have cut wood*, is in the future and is a completed action. Something will have happened in the future. *I will have cut wood* in the future.

Notice that the perfect tense, the past perfect tense, and the future perfect tenses are reflections. We are using the verb tenses to think about what has happened.

Grammar Rule 4 Simple Present Tense

This tense is used for permanent and repeated actions.

She speaks English.

Sometimes it is used to express a future action about which a decision has already been made.

My plane leaves tomorrow at 7:30 A.M.
We drive home tomorrow night.

Grammar Rule 5 Simple Past Tense

This tense is used to express an action wholly completed at some point in the past.

We lived in Germany.
I went to the movies last night.

It may be used in some conditional sentences.

If Jane trained, she would win the marathon.
It would be better, if you had decided yourself.

Grammar Rule 6 Simple Future Tense

The future tense of the verb 'will' normally looks like this.

Singular	**Plural**
I will I shall	we will we shall
you will	you will
he, she, it will	they will

Figure 4.

Exercise 12

Use two irregular verbs in the future tense as in Figure 4.

For example:

I shall bid. I will bid.	We shall bid. I will bid.
You will bid.	You will bid.
He will bid.	They will bid.

Fill in any irregular verb below.

I shall	We shall
I will	We will
You will	You will
It will	They will

I shall	We shall
You will	You will
She will	They will

Spelling Rule 1

We use contractions to combine two words to make a shorter word. Vowels and consonants may be omitted. For instance, with *I will*, we change it to *I'll*.

Here are some examples:

I'll get it.
She'll do it.
They'll ask for it.

Think of as many contractions as you can. Write down both words and the contracted form. You should be able to find more than twenty examples.

Exercise 13

Fill in the following sentences with contractions of *will*.

1) We will sail to America.____________________sail to America.

2) They will talk in the lesson.____________________talk in the lesson.

3) I will jump.______________________________jump in the leaves.

4) He will cross the river.____________________cross the river.

5) You will answer quickly.____________________answer quickly.

6) It will rain hard today.____________________rain hard today.

7) She will work in the store.____________________work in the store.

Grammar Rule 7 The Present Progressive Tense

In the *present progressive tense,* actions are written in the present.

I am resting.
The waves are splashing.

Or the actions may have begun in the past, but are still going on.

The sun is still shining.
They are just leaving the harbor.

A question in the present progressive tense may refer to a future action.

Are we going to Philadelphia tomorrow?

Exercise 14

Fill in the blanks with the present progressive tense.

1) sail We are ________________________ to America.

2) talk They are ________________________ in the lesson.

3) remember They are __________________ best.

4) jump He is ________________________ in the pile of leaves.

5) walk I am ________________________ up the stairs.

6) cross Are you ______________________ the river now?

7) answer Are you _____________________ correctly?

Write your own sentences in this tense.
Write two paragraphs in this tense.

Grammar Rule 8

The *past progressive tense* expresses an action going on during a certain time in the past.

They were driving home.
While she was looking at the game, he borrowed her bicycle.
He said he was working all day.
Yes, he was telling me this morning.

Exercise 15

Use the past progressive tense

1) sail We________________________sailing to America.

2) talk They______________________talking in the lesson.

3) remember They_________________remembering best.

4) jump He_____________jumping in the pile of leaves.

5) walk I_______________walking up the stairs.

6) cross He__________________crossing the river yesterday.

7) answer_____________________you answering correctly?

8) rain It____________________raining hard today.

9) work She__________________working in the store.

10) relax She__________________relaxing on the beach.

Write your own sentences in this tense.
Write two paragraphs in this tense.

Grammar Rule 9

The *future progressive tense* expresses a future activity beginning before and finishing after a given time.

> What will you be doing in the fall?
> I will be flying across the Atlantic Ocean.
> Will you be waiting for me?

Exercise 16

Choose the future progressive tense form of the verb to complete the sentences.

1) sail Will I be____________________to America?

2) talk What will we be______________about in the lesson?

3) remember Will he be_________________________them best?

4) jump I will be_________________________into the waves.

5) walk Will he be__________________up the stairs by Thursday?

6) cross They will be_____________________the river in April.

7) answer By June, you will be___________________quickly.

8) rain Will it be___________________hard today?

9) work Will she be_________________in the store tomorrow?

10) try Will he be__________________harder problems soon?

Write your own sentences in this tense.
Write two paragraphs in this tense.
Write a story about a river that begins in the future progressive tense.

Exercise 17

Practice multiple forms: present, present progressive, past progressive, or future progressive.

1. I _____________________calling on him tomorrow.
2. How __________________ you feeling after the first day?
3. What play _______________________ you be seeing in Scranton?
4. It rained as they___________________preparing for the picnic.
5. He______________be______________to a concert.
6. The waterfalls_____________________flowing into the fjords.

7. Where__________you be____________________tomorrow?

8. The team____________be winning by this time tomorrow.

9. When will you________________________on the sea?

10. Yes, they are___________________me this morning.

Grammar Rule 10

The *present perfect tense* is formed by the present tense of the verb *to have* and a *past participle*.

Perfect tenses do not take place at the time of the action, but in its occurrence. Something happened. There is a result; for example, you won a prize or you skied down a mountain peak in Alaska.

I have won a prize.
I have skied down the mountain.

Affirmative

The boy has eaten all the apples.
The phone has rung.
The sun has set.

Interrogative

Has the boy eaten all the apples?
Has the phone rung?
Has the sun set?

Negative

The boy has not eaten all the apples.
The phone has not rung.
The sun has not set.

Exercise 18

Underline the present perfect verbs below:

Due to unconsciously catching my foot in the spokes of my brother's bike while sitting on the handlebars on the way to school, we have both landed head first on the pavement. I have thereby broken my nose.

Grammar Rule 11

The *past perfect tense* is formed by *had* and a *past participle*. It is used with an action that is concluded before a certain time in the past. The action could also take place before another action.

The mountain lion had been here.

They had trimmed the sails.

I had finally found a way to survive in the desert.

Exercise 19

Write your own paragraph in the past perfect tense as in the example below.

Due to the foot I *had* unconsciously *caught* in the spokes of my brother's bike while sitting on the handlebars on the way to school, we *had* both *landed* head first on the pavement. I *had* thereby *broken* my nose.

Grammar Rule 12

Formed by the future tense of *to have* and a *past perfect participle*, the *future perfect tense* indicates an action that will be completed before a certain time in the future or before another action in the future.

This tense is often used with the prepositions *by*.

> It is Tuesday and I will have finished my book by Friday at 12:00 noon.
> Will you have forgotten me by then?

Exercise 20

Put the sentences into the *future perfect tense*.

1) By April 1, we___________________have sailed to France.
2) Tomorrow they___________________have talked in the lesson.
3) They___________________have remembered.
4) He___________________have jumped in the pile of leaves.
5) I_________________________have walked up the stairs.
6) Tomorrow she___________________have crossed the river.
7) The ambulance will___________________answered.
8) By Thursday, she___________________have worked in the store for one month.

Grammar Rule 13

The *present perfect progressive tense* expresses the duration of an action up to the present. The action is still continuing at the moment of speaking. It may continue into the future.

I have been writing these workbooks for five months now.

The kids have been playing touch football.

Exercise 21

Complete each sentence in the present perfect progressive tense.

1) By now, they________________been sailing for five months.

2) As usual, they have____________talking in the lesson.

3) They have been__________________their party.

4) He_______________been jumping in the pile of leaves.

5) I have_________________walking up the stairs.

6) She has________________crossing the river.

7) They______________________been answering you quickly.

8) It has been______________________hard today.

9) She has been________________in the store.

Grammar Rule 14

The *past perfect progressive tense* is formed by *had been* and the *present participle* form of the verb. It is used in the following ways:

To express the duration of an action up to a certain time in the past.

When I got to the slopes, the lift had been moving for half an hour.

To express the present perfect progressive in reported speech.

I asked him what he had been doing since he arrived in Scranton.

He told me that he had been swimming in the creek.

Exercise 22

Fill in with the past perfect progressive tense.

1) We__________________been sailing to America.
2) They________________been talking in the lesson.
3) They________________been remembering.
4) He__________________been jumping in the pile of leaves.
5) I___________________been walking up the stairs.
6) She_________________been crossing the river.
7) They________________been answering you quickly.
8) It had______________raining hard today.
9) She had been________in the store.

Grammar Rule 15

The *future perfect progressive tense* is formed by the future tense of *have* and *been* and the present participle form of the verb. It is used to express the duration of an action up to a certain time in the future.

On July 4th, we will have been living in the house for twenty-five years.

James will have been working for the railroad for five years.

By ten o'clock, I will have been driving for six hours.

Exercise 23

Put these sentences into the future perfect progressive tense.

1) On June 12th, we_____________have been sailing to America for three weeks.
2) By one o`clock, they______________have been talking in the lesson several times.
3) They will have been_______________us many times by this afternoon.
4) By dinner, he will have been_____________in the pile of leaves many times.
5) She_____________have been crossing the river three hours before we get there.

Write your own sentences in this tense.
Write two paragraphs in this tense.
Write a story that begins in the future perfect progressive tense.

The Verb Tense Matrix

	Simple	Progressive	Perfect	Perfect Progressive
Present	I walk. You walk. He walks. We walk. They walk.	I am walking. You are walking. He is walking. We are walking. They are walking.	I have walked. You have walked. He has walked. We have walked. They have walked.	I have been walking.
Past	I walked. You walked. He walked. We walked. They walked.	I was walking. You were walking. He was walking. We were walking. They were walking.	I had walked. You had walked. He had walked. We had walked. They had walked.	I had been walking.
	Simple	**Progressive**	**Perfect**	**Perfect Progressive**
Future	I shall walk. I will walk. You will walk. He will walk. We shall walk. We will walk. They will walk.	I shall be walking. I will be walking. You will be walking. He will be walking. We shall be walking. We will be walking. They will be walking.	I shall have walked. I will have walked. You will have walked. He will have walked. We shall have walked. We will have walked. They will have walked.	I shall have been walking. I will have been walking. You will have been walking. He will have been walking. We shall have been walking. We will have been walking. They will have been walking.

Figure 5

Exercise 24

Fill in Figure 6 using the verb, to speak.

	Simple	**Progressive**	**Perfect**	**Perfect Progressive**
Present	I speak. You speak. He speaks. We speak. They speak.			
	Simple	**Progressive**	**Perfect**	**Perfect Progressive**
Past				
Future				

Figure 6

Exercise 25

Fill in Figure 7 using a different irregular verb for each sentence.

	Simple	**Progressive**	**Perfect**	**Perfect Progressive**
Present	I weep. You tread. He shoots.			
	Simple	**Progressive**	**Perfect**	**Perfect Progressive**
Past				
Future				

Figure 7

Exercise 26

Write three paragraphs: one in the past tense, one in the present tense, and one in the future tense.

Exercise 27

Write three paragraphs: one in the past progressive tense, one in the present progressive tense, and one in the future progressive tense.

Exercise 28

Write three paragraphs: one in the past perfect tense, one in the present perfect tense, and one in the future perfect tense.

Exercise 29

Write three paragraphs: one in the past perfect progressive tense, one in the present perfect progressive tense, and one in the future perfect progressive tense.

Exercise 30

Write a story in the future tense.

Exercise 31

Write a story in the future progressive tense.

Exercise 32

Write a story in the past perfect tense.

Exercise 33

Write a story in the past perfect progressive tense and another story in the present perfect progressive tense.

Grammar Rule 16

Active and Passive Voice in Multiple Tenses

Tense	Active Voice	Passive Voice
Simple Present	Tim teaches his class.	This class is taught by Tim.
Present Progressive	Tim is teaching this class.	This class is being taught by Tim.
Present Perfect	Tim has taught this class.	This class has been taught by Tim.
Simple Past	Tim taught this class.	This class was taught by Tim.
Tense	**Active Voice**	**Passive Voice**
Past Progressive	Tim was teaching this class.	This class was being taught by Tim.
Past Perfect	Tim had taught this class.	The class had been taught by Tim.
Simple Future	Tim will teach this class.	This class will be taught by Tim.
Future Progressive	Tim will be teaching this class.	This class will be being taught by Tim.
Future Perfect	Tim will have taught this class.	This class will have been taught by Tim.

Figure 8

Exercise 34

Write two sentences using each tense in figure 8, each with a different verb.

Test 1 Verbs

Fill in the proper verbal form in these sentences. You can use all of the tenses we have learned so far.

cry	Why have you begun to________________?
	We were________________during the movie.
give	She had________________her best to you.
	Have you________________grandmother the mail?
reach	He was________________for the sky.
	I like to________________for my shoes.
divide	You had________________the cake four ways.
	I have________________the work equally.
try	They will have________________hard.
	You had been________________for three hours.
apply	Please________________for this job.
	We have now________________.
create	Do you want to________________a better game?
	I am________________a new doll.
fight	She has been________________for her rights.
	Last year, I________________the flu.
step	I saw the man________________onto the sidewalk.
close	The police will be________________our entrance.

I ____________________ his door.

solve Will we ____________________ the problem?

No, we will have __________________ it by this afternoon.

fly The balloon will __________________ into the clouds.

She was ____________________ her kite in Brooklyn.

tease Aren't you _______________________ him?

The boy had been ___________ his brother last night.

place The girl ____________________ the frog in the grass.

We will ____________________ the flowers in the vase.

jump Can you ______________________________ over this puddle?

She _____________________________ over it easily.

fall Have you __________________ asleep?

Thank you, my grandmother __________________ gently.

mix The baker will _________________________ the flour.

I have been ______________________ it too.

read He ________________________ his books in the tree.

I will ______________________ the play out loud.

send Have you _________________________ the nice invitation?

I had ______________________ it yesterday.

smell The skunk will ___________________ up your car.

It will be ___________________ for two more days.

buy	Have you __________ your favorite flowers?
	I have happily __________ them.
graze	The cows are always __________ on the fields.
	They __________ all day and evening.
serve	The knights __________ their Queen.
	I __________ lemonade to her.
dance	We are __________ on famous ground.
	She __________ here every afternoon.
race	The cars will __________ over desert flats.
beg	Dogs like to __________ for bones.
	I __________ you to stop the music.
rake	I was __________ the leaves as I saw the bear.
sing	Please __________ with me tomorrow.
	The minister __________ constantly.
throw	She __________ her towel.
	I had __________ it into the washing machine.
make	I believe he __________ a good joke.
	Have you __________ any progress?
skip	Will he be __________ all the way home.
	I have __________ across the room.
listen	I like to __________ to such discussions.
	Have you __________ to your sister?

Test 2 IRREGULAR VERBS

Use any of the tenses we have used so far.

become What have you____________________?
She____________________sick yesterday.

bend Can you____________________his arm?
Last year I________________________my skis.

begin The game will have_____________________in one minute.

bid The old man is____________________twenty dollars.
What have they______________________________?

beat Our team had_____________________the Swedish team.
Who has_________________________whom?

build The carpenter will have_________________fine houses.
Are you__________________________this bridge?

bear Have you_________________such difficult problems?
She is______________________the baby.

bleed His leg_____________________from the leech.
Her finger was____________________badly.

break Has your pencil tip been______________________today?
Why did you______________________your promise?

burn The fire will have__________________all night.
Have you____________________your hand?

burst The ball is__________________in the air.
The class had_________________into laughter.

cast The boy had______________________the ball to his friend.
I___________________________it into the water.

catch My brother__________ a cold last night.
We all__________ them.

dream He__________ of a big, fast Mercedes Benz.
I__________ about it, too.

dig Our dog loves to__________ up the flower beds.
She__________ it up yesterday.

Grammar Rule 17

Some verbs, such as give, tell, show, lend, get, write, pay, sell, buy, bring, make, fetch, promise, and teach take an *indirect object* and a *direct object*.

The word for the person is the INDIRECT OBJECT and is the first of the two objects; the word for the thing is the DIRECT OBJECT.

He sold *us* (indirect object) his *house* (direct object).
His mother made *Tom* a *cake*.

Exercise 35

Fill in with indirect and direct objects.

1) We will give__________ a__________ for America.
2) Will they show__________ the__________ in London?
3) They will write__________ a long__________.
4) Will I buy__________ some__________ for dinner?
5) I will bring__________ a bunch of__________.
6) He is fetching__________ a load of__________.
7) Did you promise__________ a little__________?

Adverbs

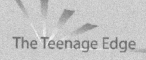

When you use an adverb, you make a verb, an adjective, or another adverb more exact in their meaning and feeling.

Adverbs often answer one of the following questions: Where? When? How? How often? To what extent?

Where?________________here, there, away, up
When?________________now, then, later, soon,
How?________________clearly, easily, quietly, slowly
How often?________________never, always, often, seldom
To what extent?________________very, too, almost, so

A. An Additional List of Adverbs

completely, swiftly, very, too dangerously, nearby, early, rarely, so long
excitedly, timely, friendly, lonely, quietly, kindly, suddenly, finally, extremely, briskly, abruptly, loudly, legibly, almost never, too abruptly, highly talented, especially well, recently, heartily, rapidly

Exercise 36

Choose ten adverbs from the list above and write ten sentences using a new adverb and a new verb in every sentence.

Write a story using as many of the adverbs in the list above as possible.

Exercise 37

Use a new adverb to define the action in the sentence.

1) She walks____________________________.

2) The boy eats____________________________.

3) The horse trots____________________________.

4) The mosquito bites____________________________.

5) The fire burns____.

6) She bade farewell____.

7) They bring food____.

8) The dam burst____.

Exercise 38

Add ten more adverbs to your vocabulary from books, newspapers, or magazines.

B. Comparison of Adverbs

Adverbs may be used in three forms called the positive, the comparative, and the superlative. Many adverbs form the latter two using –er and –est added to them. If the adverb ends in –ly, more or most are used to form the comparative and superlative forms.

Compare these adverbs: fast –faster-fastest
seldom-more seldom- most seldom
slowly-more slowly-most slowly

Exercise 39

Complete this figure.

Adverb	**Comparative**	**Superlative**
1. loud	louder	loudest
2. politely	more politely	most politely
3. happy		
4. swiftly		
5. near		
6. lively		
7. angry		
8. completely		
9. nice		

10. quick		
11. dramatically		

C. The adverbs where, when, and why

The adverbs *where*, *when,* and *why* are used in the following way:

He didn't know where the storm came from.

Will you tell me when you will be ready?

Do you know why the gate was shut and locked?

Exercise 40

Write four sentences with each of the adverbs where, when, and why.

Exercise 41

Place the adverb, provided in parentheses, in the right place in the sentence:

My friend usually plays chess.
The fish swims rapidly.

1) My brother plays football in the afternoon. (usually)

____.

2) My sister goes for a walk after dinner. (only)

____.

3) Taylor drives one of his Porsches. (rapidly)

____.

4) Halvor appears in the movie. (often)

____.

D. Well and Good

It is important to distinquish between the use of well and good. When expressing your feelings or the manner in which something is done, well is used as an adverb. She sings well.
To describe what kind of singer she is we use good as an adjective. She is a good singer.

Good may also be used as an adverb. He looked good in practice today.

Exercise 42

Decide whether to add an adjective or an adverb to complete these sentences!

1) Peter is a slow driver. He drives________________________________.
2) Mary is a quick runner. She runs_______________________________.
3) Sue is a good baker. She bakes_______________________________.
4) Fernanda sings well. She is a_____________________________singer.
5) Tom runs quickly. He is a_________________________________runner.
6) Jean smiles brightly. She has a____________________________smile.
7) Tom is a good swimmer. He swims______________________________.
8) Judy laughs spontaneously. She has_____________________________laugh.

Exercise 43

Now add these forty-three adverbs to your vocabulary. Start by writing each one in a new sentence.

quickly, clearly, splendidly, sweetly, bravely, actively, anyhow, boldly, calmly, carefully, distinctly, easily, equally, fast, gladly, how, intentionally, late, promptly, quietly, simply, sincerely, suddenly, together, willingly, wisely, wrongly, immediately, once, presently, shortly, soon, still, tomorrow, tonight, when, yesterday, yet, frequently, never, awfully, terribly, frightfully

Test 3 Adverbs

Fill in the blanks with the words from this list.

hardly, stupidly, angrily, much, beautifully, crazily, fast, slowly, creatively, happily, soon, late, fantastically, badly, well, gracefully, powerfully, usually, carefully, barely, strongly, often, seldom.

1) Our mother________________speaks.
2) The girl jumps________________.
3) My friend________________writes her homework.
4) His daughter________________rides.
5) The teacher speaks________________.
6) The clown cried________________.
7) The football player________________kicks the ball.
8) Can you laugh________________?
9) We want to work________________.
10) Remember to write________________.
11) Her dog________________barks.
12) The sun shines________________.
13) We________________learn.
14) The boat________________rides the waves.
15) The guitar wails________________.
16) The drums are pounded________________.
17) My tie flies________________in the wind.
18) Remember to hunt________________.
19) She cries________________.
20) The clown________________performs.

Conjunctions

Here are some of the most commonly used conjunctions: and, but, or, either or, neither nor, nor, not only, both, nevertheless, however, meanwhile, indeed, so, that, because, if, though, when, where, before, until, after, since, although, unless, as

Exercise 44

Find the right conjunctions.

1) ________________ you ________________ I must speak out.
2) I do not think it is a good idea, ________________ does Thea.
3) You must ________________ shoot the ball ________________ pass it.
4) It is not ________________ cold ________________ also wet.
5) I have never worked with him, ________________ I trust him.
6) He will never give up ________________ he succeeds.
7) She is behaving badly, ________________ she must leave.
8) The dog is friendly ________________ strong.
9) ________________ the boat is old, it is fun to drive.
10) My goldfish, my cat, ________________ my dog wanted to be fed.
11) ______ you eat your breakfast ________________ clean your room.
12) The cat was curious ________________ shy.
13) I like the guitar ________________ the saxophone.
14) Take it ________________ leave it.

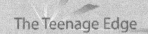

Grammar Rule 18

How to use commas in compound sentences.

Commas are also used with compound sentences. Compound sentences are two independent statements bound together by a conjunction. I run fast, and I jump high. We call the conjunctions that bind two independent sentences *coordinating conjunctions*: *for, and, nor, but, or, yet,* and *so.*

The rabbit nibbles my fingers, and it shakes its tail.

Exercise 45

Use the conjunctions *for, nor, and, but, yet, or*, and *so.*

1) The coat is soft,___________________it is warm.

2) The car is fast,____________________it is easy to drive.

3) I am listening,_____________________you are speaking.

4) Remember to walk,_____________________you will not trip.

5) I like sparrows,____________________she prefers doves.

6) The eagle soared above the lake,____________________it disappeared.

7) I asked you to be quiet,__________________you could listen to me.

8) We ran to the beach,_________she fell upon the hot sand.

9) Noah threw him the frisbee,________the wind blew it over Sam`s head.

10) I woke up early in the morning,__________I did not see the sunrise.

Interjections

Interjections express strong emotion: *O, wow, wowee, ah, sh, gosh, gee, well, hey, darn, yeah*, and *cool*, to name a few.

An exclamation point is sometimes used with an interjection, but not always.

Ah, what a beautiful sunrise.

Great! They won.

Exercise 46

Fill in the blanks with an appropriate interjection.

1.__________my, look at all the flour you have spilled on the floor.

2.__________! The Christmas lights on the trees are spectacular!

3.__________, why did you let the branch swing back at me?

4.__________, we will have a sleepover tomorrow night.

5.__________, last night the cow had her calf under our window.

6.__________! Did you see all of those meteors coming from the constellation Gemini?

7.__________! I like chocolate ice cream.

8.__________are you sure you called me?

Write ten of your own sentences with interjections.
Start two paragraphs with interjections and complete them.
Write a story about a game that begins with an interjection.

Pronouns

A. Nominative and Objective Cases

We have learned the personal pronouns that form the subject in the sentence and the objective pronouns that form the object; for example, "I speak to her." When we speak, there is someone who speaks *I* and someone who is spoken to *her.*
Those who speak are considered to be within the nominative case. They function as the subject of the sentence. In the table below you will find the nominative pronouns.

Singular		**Plural**
1st Person	I	we
2nd Person	you	you
3rd Person	he, she, it	they

Those who are spoken to are within the objective case. They function as the object of the sentence. In the table below you will find the objective pronouns.

Singular		**Plural**
1st Person	me	us
2nd Person	you	you
3rd Person	him, her, it	them

Figure 9.

If we put the nominative and objective pronouns alongside each other they look like this.

	Singular		Plural	
	Nominative	**Objective**	**Nominative**	**Objective**
1st Person	I	me	we	us
2nd Person	you	you	you	you
3rd Person	he	him	they	them
3rd Person	she	her		
3rd Person	it	it		

Figure 10.

Exercise 47

Use the right nominative or objective pronoun.

1) Today I accepted________________. Yesterday________________saw it.

2) I have seen________________. She appreciates________________.

3) Yesterday I broke________________. They have given it to________________.

4) ____________________ask me? Last Monday________________ran to school.

5) ____________________asks his sister .________have found________________.

6) ____________________takes________________into the store.

B. Relative Pronouns

The most common relative pronouns are *who, whom, whose, which, that,* and *what*.
The relative pronoun *who* defines a relationship concerning the subject.
The relative pronoun *whom* defines a relationship concerning the object.
The relative pronoun *whose* defines a possessive relationship.
The relative pronoun *which* is only used for animals and things.
The relative pronoun *that* can refer to a subject and an object. It is used for people, animals, and things.

Grammar Rule 19

Who and whom refer to people.

She is one of the women, whom I know I can trust.

Whom always relates to the object. In the sentence above *whom* relates to the object, *women*.
The sailor who spoke is my cousin.
Who always relates to the subject. In the sentence above *who* relates to the subject, *sailor*.

Exercise 48

Write four sentences using the relative pronoun, *who*.

The boy who answered the question is my friend Ken.

1. ______________________________

2. ______________________________

3. ______________________________

4. ______________________________

Exercise 49

Write six sentences using the relative pronoun, *whom*.

Mary is one of the runners, whom I know will probably win.

1. ______________________________
2. ______________________________
3. ______________________________
4. ______________________________
5. ______________________________
6. ______________________________

Exercise 50

Write five sentences using the relative pronoun, *whose*.

She is the leader whose reputation is well known.

1. ______________________________
2. ______________________________
3. ______________________________
4. ______________________________
5. ______________________________

Grammar Rule 20

The use of *which* and *that*.

Which is a relative pronoun used only for animals or things.

That is a relative pronoun used for people, animals, and things.

Exercise 51

Write ten sentences using the relative pronoun *which* for animals or things. Note the use of commas when using the relative pronoun *which*.

The goat, which stepped carefully, crossed the ledge.

Write two paragraphs using the relative pronoun *which* at least twice.
Write a story about your house, using the relative pronoun *which* at least three times.

Exercise 52

Write five sentences using the relative pronoun *that f*or people, animals, or things. Note the lack of commas used when using the relative pronoun *that*.

The boy that lives in the house on the corner is my best friend.

1. ______________________________
2. ______________________________
3. ______________________________
4. ______________________________
5. ______________________________

Write two paragraphs using the relative pronoun *that* at least twice..

Grammar Rule 21

Who may be used with animals that have a name. Note the lack of commas used here.

Our cat Chester who prowls at night is resting on the floor.
My hunting dog Kim who smelled a grouse this afternoon is sleeping now.

Exercise 53

Write five sentences using the relative pronoun *who* for animals that have a name.

His dog Tasha who behaves well is always welcome here.

1. ______________________________
2. ______________________________
3. ______________________________
4. ______________________________
5. ______________________________

Write two paragraphs using *who* for animals that have a name.

Grammar Rule 22

That may be used as the subject or the object.

That is what I mean. In this sentence *that* is the subject
We learned that yesterday. In this sentence *that* is the object.

That also modifies the subject or the object, either of which can be singular or plural.

The trout that caught the fly in the air is now diving as deep as possible.
Do you have everything that you need for the camping trip?

Exercise 54

Write eight sentences using the relative pronoun *that* in the nominative case. Note the lack of commas when using *that.*

Remember that the nominative case is the subject of the sentence.

That is what I know about Amanda.

1. ______________________________
2. ______________________________
3. ______________________________
4. ______________________________
5. ______________________________
6. ______________________________
7. ______________________________
8. ______________________________

Write two paragraphs using the relative pronoun *that* at least twice..

Write a story about your favorite store, using the relative pronoun *that* at least three times..

Exercise 55

Write five sentences using the relative pronoun *that* in the objective case.

Remember that the objectice case is used for the object of the sentence.

Do you have everything that you need for school?

1. ______________________________
2. ______________________________
3. ______________________________
4. ______________________________
5. ______________________________

Grammar Rule 23

That is used after most indefinite pronouns.

Indefinite pronouns do not name a particular person, place, or thing.

Here are some other indefinite pronouns: anything, another, any, each, everybody, everything, no one, someone, and much.

He never does anything that is wrong.
There is not much that you can do.

Exercise 56

Write five sentences using the relative pronoun *that* after the indefinite pronoun *anything*.

I will do anything that will help.

1. ______________________________
2. ______________________________
3. ______________________________
4. ______________________________
5. ______________________________

Exercise 57

Write six sentences using the relative pronoun *that* after the indefinite pronoun *much*.

There is much *that* will help.

1. ______________________________
2. ______________________________
3. ______________________________
4. ______________________________
5. ______________________________
6. ______________________________

Then find the right relative pronoun for each sentence.

1) You are the teacher____________________I respect.

2) The dog____________________owner is gone came over.

3) He is the friend____________________I count on.

4) I like the clown____________________hat falls off.

5) Is there anything____________________I can do for you?

6) Here is the boy____________________saw the fire.

7) The farmer had two oxen____________________pulled his plow.

8) He never does much____________________is wrong.

9) Rye,____________________carried me on her back, was a gentle horse.

10) My clothes____________________I wore in the rainstorm are soaking wet.

Grammar Rule 24

Understanding the use of *which* and *that.*

The relative pronouns *which* and *that* become even more complicated in their use. If you use *that,* what you are saying next is essential information to the meaning of your sentence. Therefore you do not use a comma before that.

The water that filled the basement ruined my clothes.

The goat that ran over the bridge is mine.

If you use *which*, what you are saying is not essential to the meaning of your sentence. Commas are required around the phrase using *which*.

The water, which was very cold, came from the icy creek.

The goat, which was hungry, ate very quickly.

The snake, which was coiled up, slept under the porch.

Grammar Rule 25

The use of *who*.

Who can be used with commas or without commas. It depends on the meaning of the sentence. If the information introduced by the relative prnoun *who* is not essential to the sentence you use commas. What you are saying is usually, but not always, not essential to the meaning of the sentence.

The girl, who I know, is standing over there.

Here it is not essential to the meaning of the sentence that I know the girl.

The boy who picked the blueberries sold them to us.

Here, knowing that the boy picked the berries is essential.

Exercise 58

Write five sentences using *that* with no commas, five sentences using *who* with no commas and five sentences with *which* with commas.

Prepositions

Grammar Rule 26

Prepositional phrases have no subject or verb and do not make sense if standing alone, outside of the sentence.

Practice making sentences orally with these prepositional phrases.

about the story

above the wall

across the hall

against the other team

along the river

among the enemy

at the school

by the lake

inside the train

down the slopes

through the tunnel

Exercise 59

Write prepositional phrases using the following prepositions.

about____.

above____.

across____.

against____.

along____.

among____.

at____.

beneath____.

below____.

beside____.

between____.

beyond____.

by____.

down____.

from____.

in____.

inside____.

into____.

near____.

off____.

inside____.

through____.

Exercise 60

Choose ten of the following prepositions and make a phrase, within a complete sentence, with each.

I went scuba diving under the sea to find sea stars.

over, past, round, through, to, towards, under, underneath, up, at the back, at the front, at the side, at the top, at the bottom, of, at the end of, away from, far from, between, during, for, from, in, on, since

1. ____________________
2. ____________________
3. ____________________
4. ____________________
5. ____________________
6. ____________________
7. ____________________
8. ____________________
9. ____________________
10. ____________________

Read this short introduction to one of America's forgotten heroes.

In 1869, thirty-five-year-old Major John Wesley Powell led ten men in four boats on a journey through the Grand Canyon that covered almost 1,000 miles through uncharted canyons and changed the West forever. Three months later, only five of the original company plus their one-armed Civil War hero leader emerged from the depths of the Grand Canyon at the mouth of the Virgin River.

Exercise 61

Now fill in the blanks with prepositions.

___________1869, thirty five-year-old Major John Wesley Powell led ten men________ four boats_______a journey that covered almost 1,000 miles________________ uncharted canyons and changed the West forever. Three months later, only five_____ _____the original company plus their one-armed Civil War hero leader emerged_______ from the depths_______the Grand Canyon_____the mouth______that Virgin River.

The Breaker Boys

The text below is about the breaker boys in the coalfields of Pennsylvania between 1850 and 1920. The coal cars were pulled out of the mines and hauled up to the top of the breaker, a large building where pure coal was broken down from rock and dust. The cars were emptied onto chutes below. At the bottom of the chutes on wooden boards, sat the young breaker boys between the ages of eight and fourteen. With their bare hands, they sorted the chunks of coal from the rock for eight hours a day. This was a peculiar form of child labor. They chewed tobacco to keep their mouths filled with saliva, otherwise the dust from the coal would have dried out their throats.

In their midday break, they ate lunch quickly. For the next half hour, they played football on the hard ground next to the breaker..

Exercise 62 Fill in the text with the proper prepositions.

Long iron chutes ran ___________ the top _________ the massive breaker down ___ _____ the floor. Coal cars were pulled up ______ the top _________ the breaker _____ _____ steel cables and then dumped upon a machine that moved it over ___________ the chutes where it flowed down ________ the floor. Across the chutes sat the breaker boys ______ pine boards. Black clouds _________ dust fell upon the boys as soon as the car was tipped. Their clothes turned black and their throats were filled _______ coal dust. To keep the dust out _________ their stomachs, they chewed tobacco.

Their job was to pick out the coal __________ the culm, which is useless rock. To stop the coal from flowing down the chute where they sat, they shoved their feet ________ the piles. The culm was thrown in another chute that flowed down ___________ cars waiting below. Huge piles __________ culm were deposited across the valley.

The boys were not allowed ___________ wear gloves for their bare fingers could more easily sort the coal ___________ the culm. After a day or two of work, their fingers swelled and broke open________ sores. After some weeks, their fingers were hardened for good. The foreman watched them and put a stick __________ their backs or necks if they slacked off or were caught using their secret sign language. During the hour-long lunch breaks, they would play football _________ the hard ground next _______ the breaker.

Exercise 63

Fill in the proper verbs and prepositions.

1) push — Jill ______ the boy ______ the hill.
The plow ______ the snow ______ the bank.
______ me ______ the cliff if you dare!
2) wish — Tom ______ you peace ______ the army.
3) tarry — You often ______ after school.
4) wash — I wash ______ the sink.
The machine ______ my money ______ I discovered it.
5) fish — Dad ______ far ______ the woods ______ the Shahola River.
Joe fishes ______ the lakes, ______ the river, and ______ the sea.
6) teach — Judy ______ English ______ fun, zest, and a great sense ______ humor.
7) rush — Dad ______ home. You had to rush home ______ the office.
8) finish — The boy ______ dinner. Mark ______ his work. You finish ______ dusk.
9) carry — Maria ______ the knapsack.
You are carrying me ______ the stretcher.
10) hiss — The teapot ______ the stove.
11) tarry — Jane ______ as usual ______ the way.
12) preach — Mr. Paine ______ from the pulpit.
13) hush — The mother ______ her child ______ the cradle.
14) ferry — The boat ______ us ______ the shore.
15) mash — She ______ the grapes ______ the bucket.

Write a story about a friend and use many prepositions.

Test 4 Prepositions Fill in the following sentences with prepositions.

1) We sailed ______ the American continent.
2) They talk ______ the lesson.
3) The wicker chair is ______ the green lamp.
4) I jumped ______ the pile of dead leaves.
5) I walk ______ the stairs.
6) Please put the key ______ the door quietly.
7) The path is ______ the river.
8) He was ______ friends.

9) Do not talk ______ it.
10) What you are saying is ______ the point.
11) I travel ______ car.
12) Knock ______ the door ______ entering.
13) Let us go ______ a walk.
14) Go and sit ______ your friend.
15) She lives ______ Princeton.
16) Henry's work is well ______ the average.
17) Look ______ the horizon.
18) He lives ______ Adams Street.
19) Are you ______ us?
20) She lived happily ______ them.

Finish these sentences so they make sense.

1) They suffered terribly from ______.

2) I will stay in London for ______.

3) We are looking at ______.

4) I like to speak about ______.

5) He wants to be with ______.

Write a full sentence with each preposition.

through ______.

before ______.

beneath ______.

into ______.

with ______.

among ______.

between ______.

for ______.

Exercise 64

Write in the right preposition.

1) She has been ill ________ the last year.

2) ________ May 1st, there was a big fire ________ the town.

3) My house should be finished ________ next month.

4) Tom dreamed ________ his next vacation.

5) He has been ill ________ bed ________ two weeks.

6) They will come back ________ Friday.

7) He will not be back ________ tomorrow.

8) What are you going to do ________ lunch?

9) He went to school ________ the day ________ yesterday.

We always stay ________ home Friday night.

10) ________ that moment a stranger popped his ________ the window.

11) ________ the beginning we were outnumbered.

12) My aunt has just been with us ________ two days.

13) Most birds return ________ the Spring and leave ________ the Fall.

14) He will stay here ________ two weeks.

15) Sherri has learned French ________ seven years.

16) Patrick has been sleeping ________ last night.

17) My parents have been married ________ twenty-five years.

Nouns

The Teenage Edge

A. Plurals

Common Plural Nouns

Proper nouns are the names of a particular person, place, or thing. They are usually singular. They may also be plural; for example: the *Himalayas*, the *West Indies*, the *Smiths*, or in such a sentence as, "There are three Johnsons in my class" instead of "I have three boys with the name *Johnson* in my class."

Latin Plurals change the whole word in the plural.
axis-axes, medium—media, bacterium—bacteria, radius—radii

Greek Plurals are also irregular.
analysis—analyses, basis—bases, crisis—crises, hypothesis—hypotheses, thesis—thesis, phenomenon- phenomena, criterion—criteria, oasis-oases

We have some foreign words with two plural forms in English.

curriculum—curricula, curriculums
appendix—appendixes, appendices
formula—formulae, formulas
fungus—fungi, funguses
focus—foci, focuses
minimum—minima, minimums
soprano—soprani, sopranos

Plural words from other languages are sometimes spelled the same way as plural words in English.

bonus—bonuses
chorus—choruses
circus—circuses
prospectus—prospectuses
area—areas
arena—arenas
encyclopedia—encyclopedias
era—eras

idea—ideas
peninsula—peninsulas
sonata—sonatas
solo—solos
umbrella—umbrellas
villa—villas
album—albums
museum—museums
iris - irises

Nouns with no singular form that require a plural form of a verb:
pants, clothes, shorts, drawers, pajamas, trousers
scissors, pliers, spectacles, glasses, mumps, measles
cards, dominoes, billiards
riches, scales, contents, credentials, ashes, savings, shavings

My pants are blue.
The cards are well-shuffled.

B. Collective Nouns

class, tribe, crowd, team, government, family, school

Grammar Rule 27

Collective nouns are regarded as singular and take a singular verb.

The Clarks Summit team is winning.
Our school has decided to improve the playground.

Grammar Rule 28

The following nouns are always used with a plural verb: people, police, clergy, and cattle.

The cattle are grazing.

Grammar Rule 29

If two subjects joined by *and* are considered one thing, the singular verb is used.

Bread and butter is good for you.
Bread and butter are good for you. (Notice the difference.)
That teacher and coach is inspiring. (This is one person.)
The patriot and soldier fought the war.

Exercise 65

Write sentences with ten collective nouns.

C. Possessive Nouns

The possessive nouns show the relationship between nouns in the sentence indicating ownership.

This is Jim's book.

Grammar Rule 30

For singular nouns add ('s) to show ownership.

the hen's egg

Jim - Jim's This is Jim's hammer.
Girl - girl's I like the girl's tuba.

Grammar Rule 31

To form the possessive with names ending in *s*, or the *s* or *z* sound, adding apostrophe *s* is preferred.

The Jones's swimming pool is open.
Lucas's new belt has a silver buckle
The Mercedes Benz´s reputation is strong.

Grammar Rule 32

With plural nouns, find the plural form of the noun first.

boy, boys woman, women

Grammar Rule 33

If the plural noun ends in *s*, add the apostrophe **(´).**

The boys' basketball team wins.

My sisters' room is huge.

Grammar Rule 34

If the plural noun does not end in *s*, add apostrophe ('s).

The women´s soccer team loses!

Exercise 66

Use each lake from North American geography in a sentence, in the possessive form.

Lake Superior's water is very cold.

Along Lake Powell's shore, we find sharp rocks.

Mackinac Island is one of Lake Michigan's most famous attractions.

Lake Huron

____

Lake Tahoe

____

Lake Okeechobee

____

Lake Placid

____

Lake Winnebago

____

Lake of the Woods

____

Exercise 67

Use each ocean, river, sea, gulf, bay, and mountain range from North American geography in a sentence in the possessive form.

The Pacific Ocean's waves are powerful and loud.

We prefer the Atlantic Ocean's salmon.

Bering Sea

____

Caribbean Sea

____

Gulf of Mexico

____

Appalachian Mountains

____

James Bay

____

Hudson Bay

____

Delaware Bay

____

Rocky Mountains

____

Chesapeake Bay

____

Teton Mountains

____

Columbia River

____

Adjectives

Now we practice the positive, comparative, and superlative forms of English adjectives.

Positive	**Comparative**	**Superlative**
short	shorter	shortest
wise	wiser	wisest
happy	happier	happiest
big	bigger	biggest
large	larger	largest
old	older	oldest
hot	hotter	hottest
smart	smarter	smartest
clear	clearer	clearest
soft	softer	softest
Positive	**Comparative**	**Superlative**
pretty	prettier	prettiest
simple	simpler	simplest
narrow	narrower	narrowest
quiet	quieter	quietest
handsome	handsomer	handsomest

Grammar Rule 35

To create the comparative and superlative form in one-syllable adjectives with a single consonant after a single vowel, double the consonant and add *er* or *est*. This is sometimes called the *Doubling Rule*.

big—bigger - biggest

Spelling Rule 2

To form the comparative and superlative form in all one-syllable and two-syllable adjectives that end with *y*, you change the *y to i* and add the suffix. This is called the *Y Rule*.

pretty—prettier - prettiest

Spelling Rule 3

If words end in *ow*, to make the comparative or superlative you add *er* or *est* at the end.

slow—slower—slowest

Grammar Rule 36

All other two-syllable adjectives are formed with *more* or *most*. Some adjectives that use *more* and *most:*

Positive	Comparative	Superlative
honest	more honest	most honest
useful	more useful	most useful
wicked	more wicked	most wicked
tempting	more tempting	most tempting
difficult	more difficult	most difficult
beautiful	more beautiful	most beautiful
interesting	more interesting	most interesting
splendid	more splendid	most splendid
helpful	more helpful	most helpful
fertile	more fertile	most fertile
extravagant	more extravagant	most extravagant

Figure 11.

Irregular Adjectives

Positive	Comparative	Superlative
good	better	best
bad	worse	worst
old	older, elder	oldest, eldest
far	farther, further	farthest, furthest
late	later, latter	latest, last
little	less, lesser	least
near	nearer	nearest, next
much, many	more	most
out	outer	outermost
up	upper	uppermost
in	inner	innermost
fore	former	foremost, first

-ous

Positive	Comparative	Superlative
famous	more famous	most famous
joyous	more joyous	most joyous
obnoxious	more obnoxious	most obnoxious
tremendous	more tremendous	most tremendous
anxious	more anxious	most anxious
adventurous	more adventurous	most adventurous

-some

Positive	Comparative	Superlative
handsome	more handsome	most handsome
burdensome	more burdensome	most burdensome
lonesome	more lonesome	most lonesome
troublesome	more troublesome	most troublesome

-tional

Positive	Comparative	Superlative
national	more national	most national
international	more international	most international
emotional	more emotional	most emotional
exceptional	more exceptional	most exceptional
rational	more rational	most rational

Figure 12.

Exercise 68

Fill in the missing forms of the positive, comparative, or superlative.

Positive	Comparative	Superlative
tall		
	better	
		longest
		ugliest
	more beautiful	
fast		
		oldest
slow		
	longer	
fat		
	thinner	
		youngest

Positive	Comparative	Superlative
		cheapest
difficult		
	easier	
expensive		
	earlier	
		latest
heavy		
	lighter	
stupid		

Exercise 69

Write ten sentences, each with one form of the adjectives above.

Exercise 70

Use each one of these descriptions of birds in a sentence.

reddest markings____.

mostly white____.

outer feathers____.

long bill____.

dusky brown____.

pure red____.

yellow stripe____.

white patch on the wing__________________________________.

purer white____.

melted with light brown__________________________________.

light, blue stripes_______________________________________.

Exercise 71

Write sentences with these verbs in either the present, past, or perfect tenses with new adjectives each time.

begin____.

blow____.

break____.

bring____.

build____.

blow____.

do____.

run____.

care____.

choose____.

write____.

leave____.

spy____.

Grammar Rule 37

Commas never separate one adjective from its noun.

The warm sand fell across her toes.

Grammar Rule 38

When there are multiple adjectives used before a noun, it may be necessary to separate them with a comma. We use commas when the adjectives equally modify the noun and can be interchanged.

She wrapped a towel around her shivering, wet boy. You could have written this sentence using a conjunction.

She wrapped a towel around her wet *and* shivering boy.

Grammar Rule 39

There is an established, conventional order to the placement of adjectives before a noun. Using adjectives in this way does not require a comma to separate them. The conventional order is to place them from the most particular to the most general.

We say *the big, round ball*, not *the round, big ball.*

Let us build a sentence using the correct order. In this example, we start with the number, then the opinion, the size, and finally the age to describe our cars.

We have three cars. (number of cars)

We have three, fancy cars. (number of cars and opinion)

We have three, fancy, large cars. (number of cars, opinion, and size)

We have three, fancy, large, new cars. (number of cars, opinion, size, and age of the cars)

If we had not followed the order, we might have written a sentence about the car such as this: We have fancy, new, large, three cars.

Here is the accepted order for using adjectives.

number (sixteen, many, a) > *opinion* (useful, stylish, juicy) > *size* (huge, small) > *age* (new, ancient) > *shape* (round, square) > *color* (blue, green) > *origin* (American, Sears) > *material* (plastic, cotton) > *purpose* (fun, play)

number > opinion > size > age > shape > color > origin > material > purpose

Exercise 72

Write five of your own sentences with multiple adjectives in the correct order.

Grammar Rule 40

The articles *the, an*, and *a* are used as adjectives.

I have an aunt in Philadelphia.

You are a good friend.

Give me the ball and I will score a touchdown.

Exercise 73

Write three sentences with each article used as an adjective.

Punctuation Rules

The Teenage Edge

A. Rules for Writing Dialogue/Direct Speech

1. Whenever someone speaks, quotation marks are put around what they say.

   James said, "I rode the train from Florida to Texas."

   "We need to be careful," James commented, "the train is due soon."

   "Step back, here it comes!"

2. In American dialogue, the quotation marks used are usually double: (")

3. All ending punctuation marks go inside the quotation marks.

4. Capitalize the first word that is said.

   "It is impressive to see it go by," said Christopher.

5. A specific part refers to the speaker: "said Christopher," "said he," "said she," and so forth. This is called a tag.

   The tag, when at the end of the sentence, has a period after it.

"I like it too," replied James.

6. If the sentence would normally end with a period, but continues on, change the period to a comma.

   "Let us stay awhile," James said, "in case another train comes."

7. But if it ends in an exclamation mark or a question mark, it can stay as is.

   "Stop!" he yelled.

   "Are you coming soon?" she asked.

8. If the dialogue is interrupted by a tag, put a semicolon after the tag and start the rest of the sentence with a lower case letter, unless it is a proper noun, or put a period after the tag and begin the new sentence with a capital letter.

   "Let's come back this afternoon," James said; "we may see another."

   "Let's come back this afternoon," James said. "We may see another."

   "Okay James," Christopher said, "Dalton Station will be my destination, if my mom lets me."

9. Start a new paragraph each time someone speaks in a dialogue.

   Christopher yelled as he approached the station, "Did you hear that?"

   "Yes, a train whistle," called James from down the lane.

"How far away do you think it is?" Christopher asked.

B. Other Punctuation Rules

Punctuation Rule 1

Remember there are three kinds of ending punctuation: the period (.), the exclamation sign (!), and the question mark(?).

Ending punctuation does just that; it ends the sentence or statement.

We arrived a little too late.
Stop the car!
What do you want?
Go!

Punctuation Rule 2

The period (.) is also used at the end of abbreviations and initials.

Mr.	Mister
Mrs.	Madam
Ms.	Miss
Nov.	November
J. T. Walsh	James Taylor Walsh
e.g.	that is
etc.	etcetera
Dr.	Doctor

Punctuation Rule 3

The question mark is used after a direct question, but not after an indirect one.

Where is the best snow?
I asked if you were running this morning.

Direct: I said to her, "Where are you going this afternoon?"
Indirect: I asked her where she was going this afternoon.

Punctuation Rule 4

A. The colon is used when writing time.

6:00
5:38

B. A colon is used after the greeting of a business letter.

Dear Mr. Jones:

C. A colon introduces or defines something. It also can be used to introduce a list of items.

Please welcome our trout-fishing expert: Mr. Todd.

These are my favorite team sports: football, baseball, and basketball.

We have very good dancers: Manny, Ruben, Carlos, Anna, and Sherifia.

Punctuation Rule 5

Semicolons

A semicolon links two independent statements that could stand alone.

For example: It is cold outside; the wind is blowing seriously.

Punctuation Rule 6

All proper nouns are capitalized: names of people, days of the week, months, place names for cities, states and countries, businesses, and abbreviations.

Punctuation Rule 7

Capital letters are used for adjectives that form proper nouns.

American sports
The Chinese language
Alexander the Great

Punctuation Rule 8

Capital letters are used for the first word of each line of poetry.

"I'll send him to the mainland then, to Sparta
By the sand beach Pylos; let him find
News of his dear father where he may
And win his own renown about the world."
From the "The Odyssey" by Homer

Punctuation Rule 9

Commas are used with conjunctions when a series of items is listed.

I like licorice, toffee, and jawbreakers.

When joining two independent statements with a coordinating conjunction such as *for, and, nor, but, or, yet*, and *so* you do use commas.

We hiked up Mt. George, and then we climbed Trouble Rock.

Punctuation Rule 10

Commas used to separate an introductory item from the rest of the sentence.

With a noun of direct address- Beth, are you sure you remember how to cook?

With an adverb- Proudly, she showed her pink bracelet to her friend.

With a speaker tag- Seth shouted, "I caught the frog!"

With *yes* and *no.*

Yes, I will do it.

No, I will not.

Punctuation Rule 11

Commas are used to indicate direct address.

Shelly, will you bring me some carrots from the garden?

Punctuation Rule 12

Commas are used to set off a 'tag' question from the rest of the sentence.

A tag question is a short question that we use when we want a yes or no answer or to establish something.

You'll do it, won't you?

He answered correctly, didn't he?

Punctuation Rule 13

A comma may be used with interjections. It deemphasizes the impact of the interjection.

'Yes, I will help you.' as opposed to 'Yes! We won!'

Punctuation Rule 14

Indicate titles of works by underlining, quotation marks, or italics.

a. When writing by hand, you underline the title.

b. Italics are used for lengthy works, complete works, or a collection of short works.

Sacajawea

The Chronicles of Narnia

Canterbury Tales

c. Quotation marks are used to indicate parts of long works: book chapters, tv show episodes, poems, and short works.

"Sixty Minutes"

" I am Collin" from *The Secret Garden*

"The Odyssey"

Frequently Confused Words

We often confuse words that sound similar, but are spelled differently.

affect, effect

ant, aunt

ate, eight

all ready, already

clothes, close

cent, scent, sent

dew, do, due

dear, deer

die, dye

feat, feet

flour, flower

four, for, fore

no, know

their. there

to, two, too

tow, toe

Exercise 74

Write sentences with each set of words above that sound the same but are spelled differently.

Here are more frequently confused words:

forth, fourth,

I'll, aisle, isle

lead, led,

lain, lane

marry, merry

pail, pale

passed, past

plain, plane

rain, reign, rein

right, rite, write

scene, seen

vary, very

waist, waste

weak, week

weather, whether

which, witch

whose, who's

your, you're, yore

hare, hair

knew, new

knight,night

lie, lye

one, won

pair, pare, pear

peace, piece

presence, presents

red, read

road, rode, rowed

sea, see

threw, through

Arthur, author

wear, ware

we're, were

hole, whole

wood, would

Exercise 75

Pick eight pairs of words that sound the same and write their meanings. Then use them in sentences.

Writing Letters

When writing to a friend you write the date at the top right of the letter. You do not need to write the address of the friend. Indent your paragraphs five spaces.

October 27, 2013

Dear Terry,

The snow is falling heavily and the lakes are frozen! Now we get to ski on the lakes and fly down the hills on our toboggans.

It was so nice to hear from you in Boston. You must be happy to meet new people and study in a city with more than thirty colleges! Make sure you get a pastrami sandwich today on your walk back to your dorm. I usually did that in Cambridge.

Good luck with your finals next week. We are so proud of you and know you are enjoying these big challenges.

We have little news in the valley. Work is busy and demanding. Our mother is in charge of an entire floor at the hospital and doing well. Grandpa and Grandma walk every day on the icy roads. They make their daily soup as you know.

Our state is still spending too much money. We are concerned because no one knows where the deficits will lead us. Someday the bill will have to be paid.

I am off to the movies now. You know how much I love them!

We miss you.

Yours truly,
Ted

Writing A Business Letter

When writing a formal letter, using the indented form, you place your address at the top right of the letter with the date below. You put the name and the address of the person whom you are writing below and to the left. Each paragraph is indented five spaces. The closing goes at the end of the letter, below the section with your address and date.

438 Hill Rd.
Waverly, Pa. 18943

March 14, 2015

Ms. Alice Bark
California Tourist Bureau
348 Orchard Ave.
Sacramento, Ca. 96854

Dear Ms. Bark:

Our fifth grade class is doing state reports. I chose California because my mom is from there. She lived in Santa Cruz for many years.

Would you send me any tourist materials: maps, brochures, or pamphlets that you might have about your state? If you can send them soon, that would be helpful. Thank you for your help.

Sincerely,
Helen James

Congratulations, now you have completed this workbook!

Please contact me at:

Ted Warren

www.teenage-edge.org

email: ted.warren@teenage-edge.org

Lightning Source UK Ltd.
Milton Keynes UK
UKHW030636270221
379408UK00005B/153

9 780991 584727